Shipwreck at Old Jelly's Farm

Written by Martin Waddell
Illustrated by Graham Philpot

Old Jelly lived on a farm, with Big Nelly.
So did the cow.

One day it rained
and it rained and it rained.

Jelly and Nelly hid in the house.
So did the cow.

But Nelly opened the door . . .
and **whoosh!**
The water came into the house . . .

and went out the back door.

Jelly and Nelly sailed out of the house,
sitting on Jelly's big table.
So did the cow.

Jelly and Nelly sailed out of the gate.
So did the cow.

Jelly and Nelly sailed out of the village.
So did the cow.

They were shipwrecked!
So was the cow.

Jelly and Nelly looked at the water.
So did the cow.

Jelly and Nelly climbed up the tree.

So did the cow.

But the water climbed too.

It wet Jelly's toes.

It wet Nelly's nose . . .

then it went down!

Jelly and Nelly were stuck
at the top of the tree.
So was the cow.

Splat!
Jelly jumped down.

Splat!
Nelly landed on Jelly.

Splat!

The cow landed on Jelly and Nelly.

Jelly and Nelly were covered in mud.
So was the cow.

Jelly and Nelly slid down the hill to the house.
So did the cow.

Jelly and Nelly got lots of soap.
They jumped in the duckpond
and washed the mud off.

So did the cow!

Then Jelly and Nelly built a new house
at the top of the hill.

They are living there still.
And so is the cow!